Phonics
Sticker
Activity Book

This phonics sticker activity book belongs to:

Millie and Frankie

owton and ottie

Illustrated by Mike Phillips and Sue King

Notes for parents and teachers:

Ladybird's **Phonics Sticker Activity Book** encourages your child to enjoy reading, spelling and writing simple words by building them up from their separate sounds (c-a-t) and blends (f-i-sh).

How to use this activity book:

• Work through the activities with your child, doing a little at a time and keeping your sessions light-hearted and fun. Five or ten minutes a day is ideal.
• Use the letter sounds - a b c rather than their names ABC. For example, use a as in apple, b as in box and c as in cup, rather than ay bee cee.
• Talk about the sounds and letters practice your child is doing in school to make sure you work on the appropriate pages in this activity book.
• Make sure your child is sitting comfortably when she writes.

This activity book covers a wide range of learning, from short vowels as in cat and fox, through to consonant blends such as ng, ck, sh, mp and long vowel sounds such as bear and air.

fox in a box

This section of the book:
- focuses on the early stages of phonics
- introduces simple words with short vowel sounds like cat and dog
- encourages word-building with letters and sounds.

Written by Carol Gray

Beginnings

Say the sound that begins each of these words.
Then write the letter that matches that sound.
The first one has been done for you.

m

b

p

s

f

b

m

j

t

Fat Cat's page

Listen out for the a sound!

c-a-t

Write the first letter to complete each word.

b ag

m an

c at

t ap

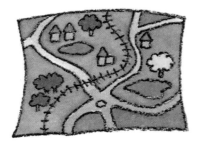

m ap

J am

Copy the -at ending to finish these rhyming words.

c at

b at

h at

r at

Red Hen's page

Write the first letter
to complete each word.

Get set for the e sound!

h-e-n

bed

n et

h en

l eg

p eg

w eb

Copy the -en ending to finish these rhyming words.

h_en_

m_en_

t_en_

p_en_

Big Pig's page

Write the first letter
to complete each word.

My page is for
things with i in!

p-i-g

s ix

x in

p ig

b in

_ ip

_ ig

Copy the -ig ending to finish these rhyming words.

p ig   w __   b __   d __

Top Dog's page

Write the first letter
to complete each word.

Can you spot
lots of o words?

_op

_ot

d-o-g

dog

_ot

_ox

_ox

Copy the -og ending to finish these rhyming words.

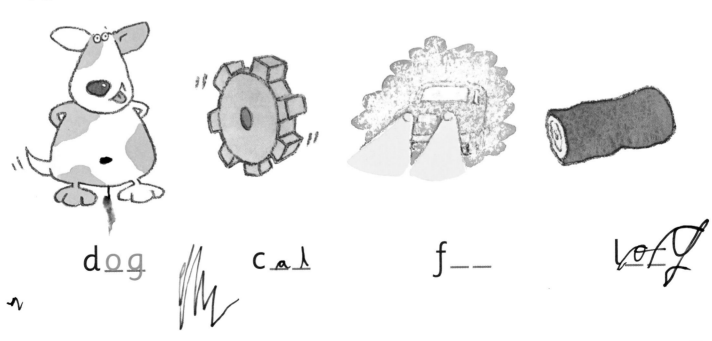

dog

cog

f__

log

9

Fun Bug's page

Write the first letter
to finish each word.

Stuff with u in is fun!

b-u-g

jug

_un

<u>b</u>ug

<u>c</u>up

<u>s</u>um

_ut

Copy the -ug ending to finish these rhyming words.

b<u>ug</u>   j<u>ug</u>   m<u>ug</u>   r<u>ug</u>

Which is the word?

Read the words in each line. Listen to the sound. Now draw a ring round the word that matches each picture.

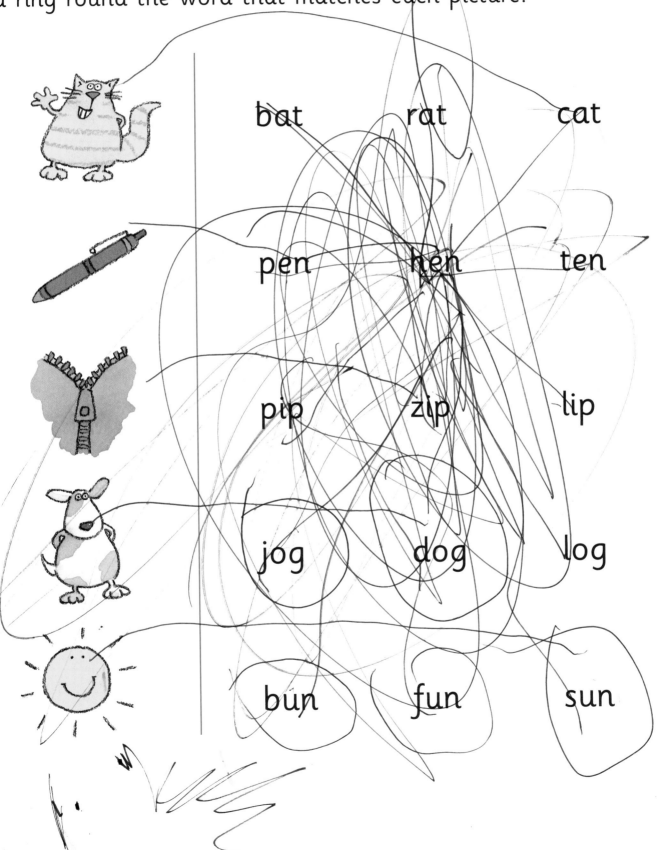

bat   rat   cat

pen   hen   ten

pip   zip   lip

jog   dog   log

bun   fun   sun

Pick a middle

Write the correct middle letter
to complete each word.

I'm a bug in
a big bag!

a or e?

b᷾g

p_n

m_n

b᷾g

p_n

m_n

a or i?

fᴧt

p_t

t_p

fᴧt

pᴧt

t_p

12

r _ g

b _ g

t ᴀ g

r _ g

b _ g

t ᴀ g

a or o?

m _ p

c ᴀ t

h _ t

m _ p

c ᴀ t

h u r t

e or u?

b e d

n u t

o or i?

d _ g

b e d

n e t

d o g

13

Is this the end?

Say the word for each picture. Listen to the last letter sound.
Now choose and write the correct ending for each word.

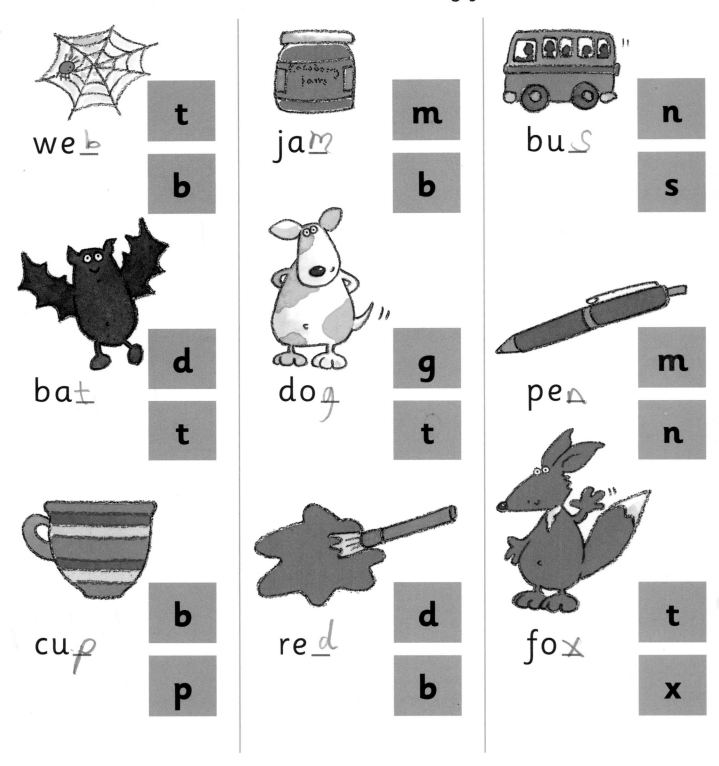

we_b_   **t**
         b

ja_m_   **m**
         b

bu_s_   **n**
         s

ba_t_   **d**
         t

do_g_   **g**
         t

pe_n_   **m**
         n

cu_p_   **b**
         p

re_d_   **d**
         b

fo_x_   **t**
         x

The ch sh and th sounds

Sometimes a sound is represented by more than one letter.
Use the pairs of red letters to complete the words in each box.
Read the words and listen to the sounds the letters make.

sh

shed   ship   shop   shot

dish   fish   rash   rush

th

bath   moth

cloth   thin

ch

chip   chop

chin   rich

What's going on?

Read each sentence, then find a sticker that matches each one.

Pig dug a
big pit.

Fox hid in
the red box.

Cat and Dog
sat in the sun.

Bug ran up
to the top.

duck in a truck

This section of the book:
- continues work on the early stages of phonics
- introduces simple words with common combinations of consonants, such as king, stamp and blink.

Written by Dilys Ross

Encourage your child to ask for help whenever it is needed.

What's that sound?

Say what you see in each picture. Listen to the sounds at the ends of the words.

duck

clock

brick

neck

wall

bell

hill

doll

dress

cross

class

kiss

ck , ll **or** ss

Now write either ck, ll or ss to finish each word correctly.

be_ _

bri_ _

do_ _

ki_ _

clo_ _

cla_ _

du_ _

dre_ _

ne_ _

cro_ _

hi_ _

wa_ _

Odd one out

Three things in each box begin with the same sound.
Say what you see, then cross through the odd one out.
Trace over the letters with a pencil to spell the sound.

tr

bl

dr

pl

pr

gr

Which is the word?

Read the words in each line. Draw a ring round the one that matches each picture.

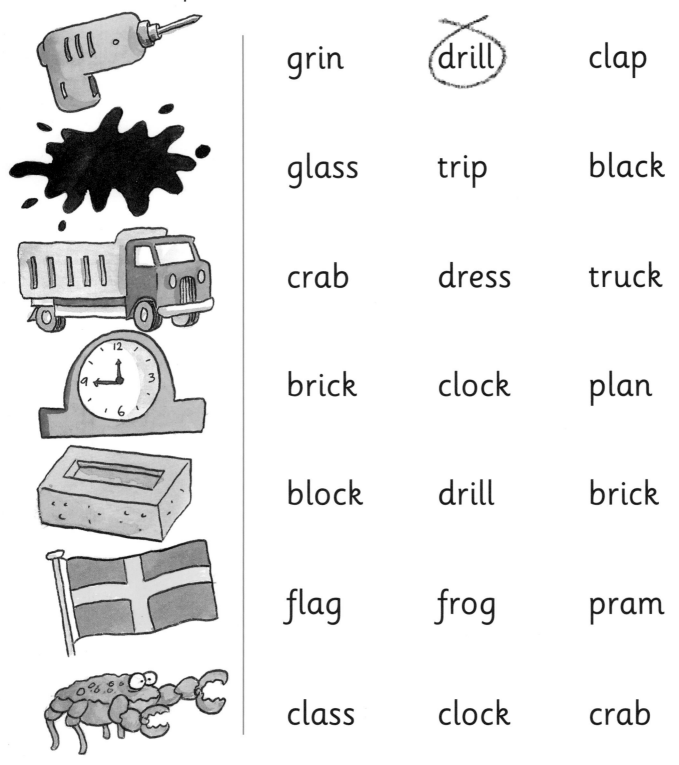

grin	drill	clap
glass	trip	black
crab	dress	truck
brick	clock	plan
block	drill	brick
flag	frog	pram
class	clock	crab

Pick a beginning

Say the word for each picture. Listen to the beginning sound.
Now choose and write the correct spelling pattern.

br
bl
___ock

fr
fl
___og

pl
pr
___am

gl
gr
___ass

br
bl
___ick

cl
cr
___oss

pr
pl
___um

cl
cr
___ock

gr
gl
___ass

Rhyme and spell

Look at the pictures. How many of the rhyming pairs of words can you fill in?

f r o g / d o g

_ _ _ _ / f l a g

_ _ _ _ / _ _ _ _

b u s h / _ _ _ _

b u s h i s / _ _ _ _

_ _ _ _ / _ _ _ _

_ _ _ _ _ / _ _ _ _

_ _ _ _ _ / _ _ _ _

Snakes and spiders

Say what you see in each box, and listen to the beginning of the word. Can you find three other words that begin the same way? Copy them into the box, and read them aloud.

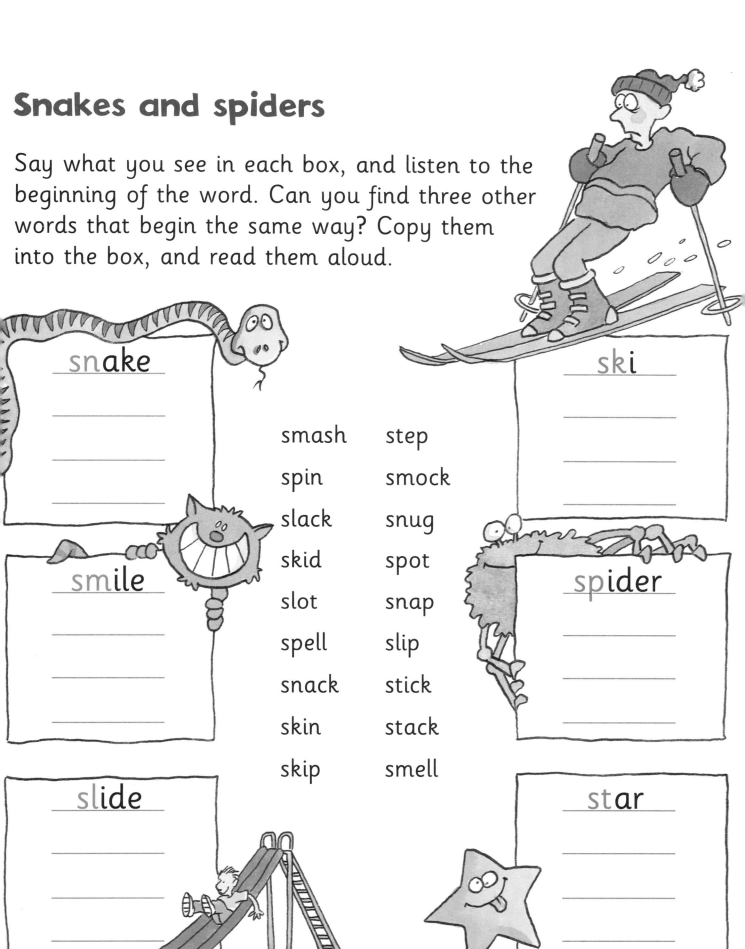

snake

ski

smash   step
spin   smock
slack   snug
skid   spot
slot   snap
spell   slip
snack   stick
skin   stack
skip   smell

smile

spider

slide

star

25

Pick a spelling

Choose the correct spelling to complete each word below.

sm or sl?

___im   ___ell   ___ash   ___ip

sn or sk?

___ip   ___ack   ___ap   ___id

sp or st?

___in   ___ot   ___ep   ___ick

Pick an ending

Look at this picture and read the words below it. What sounds do the red letters make?

a <u>king</u> in a <u>vest</u>

Now use either ng or st to finish each of these words.

ne＿＿   swi＿＿   che＿＿   ri＿＿

ha＿＿   go＿＿   du＿＿   wi＿＿

re＿＿   li＿＿   si＿＿   fi＿＿

nt and nd

Say what you see in each box. Listen to the endings.

| tent | stunt | ant | mint |

| pond | hand | friend | wind |

Now fill in the endings for these words. Under each one, write the word from above that rhymes with it.

pa__   me__   spri__   ba__

____   ____   ____   ____

mp, nk **and** nch

Say what you see below, and listen to the ending of each word.

jump

sink

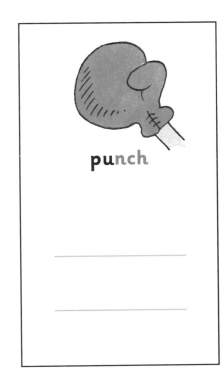

punch

Now read these words aloud. Find the stickers and place each one into the correct box above, to make three lists of rhymes.

link

hump

lunch

pink

drink

bunch

stump

bump

29

Rhyme and spell

See how many of these pairs of rhyming words you can spell.

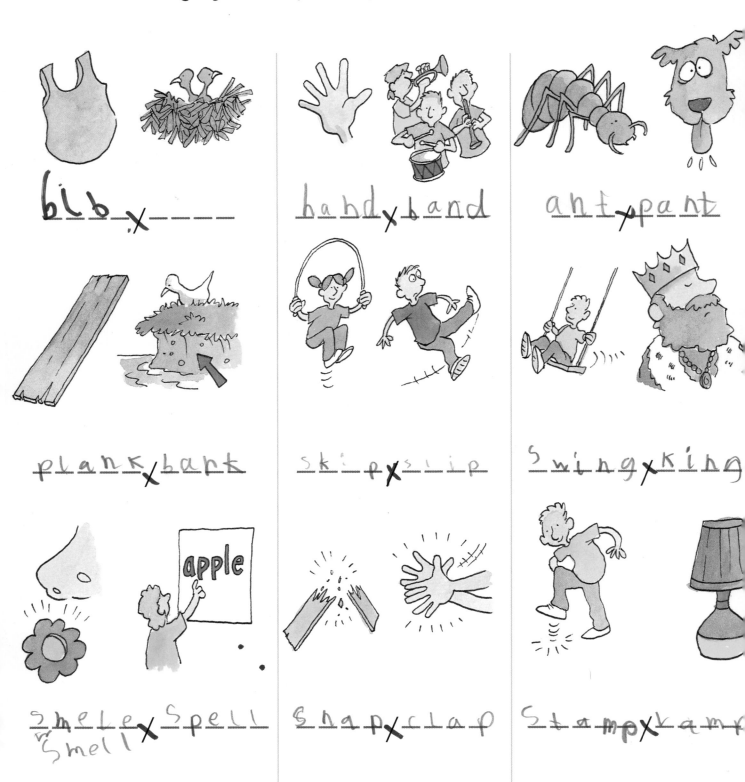

bib x _____

hand x band

ant x pant

plank x bark

skip x slip

swing x king

smelex spell
smell x

snap x clap

stamp x lamp

More endings

Here are some other endings you might hear. Say what you see and listen to the end sounds. Trace over the red letters with a pencil to write each spelling pattern.

raft

milk

belt

desk

act

crisp

help

script

gold

shelf

next

flask

Springs and strings

Some beginning sounds are spelt with three letters. Read these words aloud and look at the red spelling patterns.

scrub   string   split

spring   three   shrug

Now see if you can read these sentences, and find the correct sounds to complete them.

My best red vest has s c r _ _ unk!

Jack is very s t r ong.

Can you s p r int as fast as me?

I like to jump in with a s p l ash!

The t h r ush sang a song.

Have you lost this s c r ap of paper?

What's going on? (page 16)

mp, nk **and** nch (page 29)

	hump	lunch	pink
bunch	bump	stump	drink

Hear the sounds (page 34)

link

Hear the sounds (page 35)

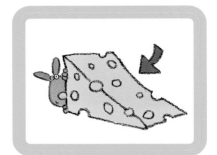

The blue spook's page (page 40)

Large Shark's page (page 54)

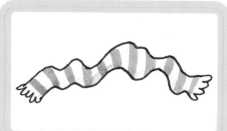

Short Horse's page (page 58)

sc**ore**

fl**oor**

s**aw**

d**oor**

cl**aw**

sn**ore**

Cow and Bear at the fair (pages 62 and 63)

purple

noise

target

Bear

crowd

girl

Cow

fair

boy

car

saw

darts

dark

sauce

paws

toy

sheep in a heap

This section of the book:
- continues work on the early stages of phonics
- introduces simple words which include long vowel sounds such as day, sleep and boat.

Written by Dick Crossley

Encourage your child to ask for help whenever it is needed.

Hear the sounds

Say what you see in each row, and listen to the end sound that the two words share.
Find a sticker with the same end sound, and place it in the row.

Look at the pictures in each row. Say what you see, and listen to the middle sound. Now choose a sticker that has the same middle sound and place it in the row.

The play train page

Use the ay spelling pattern to finish these words. Say each word and listen to the end sounds.

play   d __ __   tr __ __

pr __ __   spr __ __   h __ __

Now use the ai spelling pattern to complete these words.

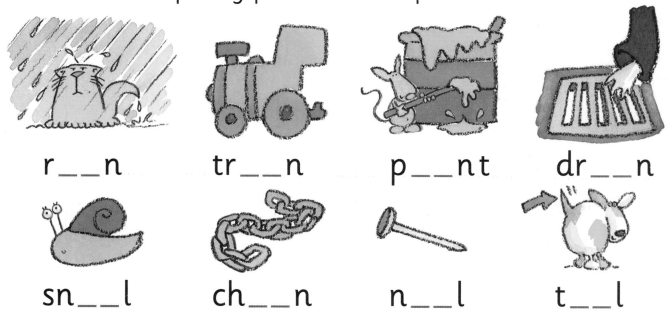

r __ __ n   tr __ __ n   p __ __ nt   dr __ __ n

sn __ __ l   ch __ __ n   n __ __ l   t __ __ l

Can you find three ai words that rhyme in each row?

The mean queen's page

Use the ea spelling pattern to complete each word.
Circle the words that match each picture.

m _ _ l

cr _ _ m

h _ _ t

p _ _

b _ _ ch

str _ _ m

st _ _ m

b _ _ k

p _ _ ch

b _ _ n

s _ _ l

m _ _ n

Now use the ee spelling pattern to complete these words.

sh _ _ p

gr _ _ n

sw _ _ t

h _ _ l

f _ _ t

sl _ _ p

p _ _ l

qu _ _ n

Draw a line to find the four pairs of ee words that rhyme. The first one is done for you.

The shy knight's page

Say each word and listen to the end sounds.
Trace over the red letters to write three patterns
that can spell this sound.

sky   tie   high

Now read these words and write each one under its picture.

| night | fight | light | fly | cry | shy | pie | lie |

_ _ _ _ _   _ _ _ _ _   _ _ _ _ _   _ _ _ _ _

_ _ _ _ _   _ _ _ _ _   _ _ _ _ _   _ _ _ _ _

The slow toad's page

Use the ow spelling pattern to finish each of these words, then read them aloud.

rainb___   sn___   wind___

elb__   r__   yell__

Use the oa pattern to complete these words.

b___t   g___t   s__p   c__t

t__d   t__st   r__d   l__d

Draw circles round the three oa words that rhyme in each row.

The blue spook's page

Listen to the sound at the end of each word.
Trace over the red letters with a pencil to write three patterns that spell this sound.

zoo   screw   blue

Now find the correct sticker for each of the words below.

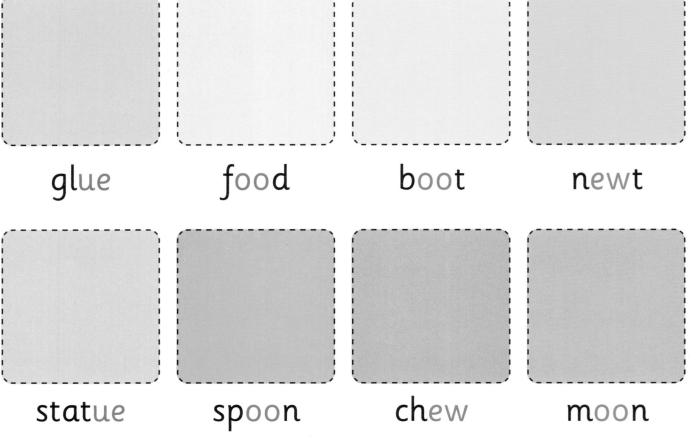

glue   food   boot   newt

statue   spoon   chew   moon

Long vowels with 'e'

Copy the vowel (a, e, i, o or u) from the first word in each pair into the second and add an e at the end. Say what you see, and listen to how the middle sound changes.

kit   k_ite_   tap   t_p_

cub   c_b_   hop   h_p_

man   m_n_   win   w_n_

More long vowels with 'e'

Here are some more long vowel words that end in e.
Use the ending of the first word in each row to complete
the rhyming words.

lake   c____   sn____   r____

hive   d____   f____   dr____

date   pl____   g____   sk____

cone   b____   st____   thr____

cave   gr____   sh____   s____

Missing middles

What sound is missing from the middle of each of these words?
Choose between the two spelling patterns to complete each one.

ee or oo?

sw__p

sh__t

t___th

sw__p

sh__t

t__th

ch__se

p__l

st__l

ch__se

p__l

st__l

More missing middles

s __ __ l

s __ __ l

m __ __ l

m __ __ l

b __ __ t

b __ __ t

igh or oo?

r __ __ __ __ t

r __ __ t

oo or ai?

t __ __ l

t __ __ l

oa or ea?

r __ __ d

r __ __ d

igh or ee?

f __ __ t

f __ __ __ t

44

Which end is which?

Choose the correct ending to finish all four words in each rhyming list.

ew, ow or ie ?

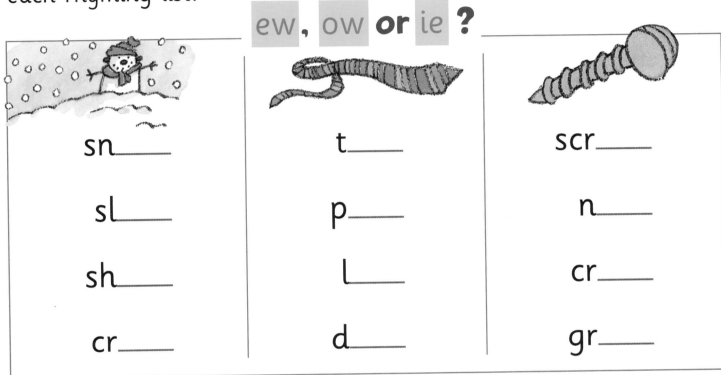

sn___	t___	scr___
sl___	p___	n___
sh___	l___	cr___
cr___	d___	gr___

ue, ay or y ?

tr___	gl___	cr___
pl___	tr___	dr___
st___	bl___	tr___
pr___	cl___	fl___

Pick a spelling

Fit the spelling patterns into each pair of words to finish them.

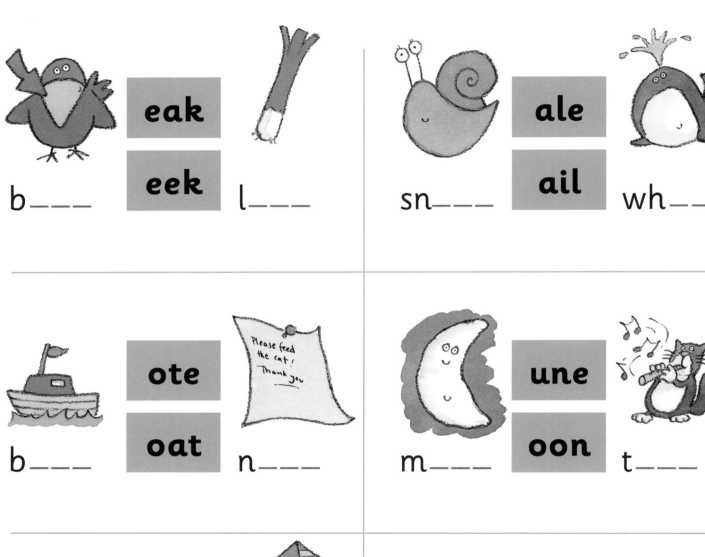

b ____   **eak**   **eek**   l ____

sn ____   **ale**   **ail**   wh ____

b ____   **ote**   **oat**   n ____

m ____   **une**   **oon**   t ____

n ____   **ight**   **ite**   k ____

s ____   **eet**   **eat**   f ____

b____   **ate**   **ait**   g____

g___   **oal**   **ole**   m____

n____   **ude**   **ood**   f____

sh____   **eap**   **eep**   l___

tr____   **ane**   **ain**   pl____

t___   **oad**   **ode**   c____

47

cl**een**/**ean** gr____

afr**aid**/**ade** sp____

s**ope**/**oap** r____

fl**ute**/**oot** b____

h**eal**/**eel** m____

cl**oak**/**oke** sm____

Section 4

bear in the air

This section of the book:
- continues to develop the phonic approach to reading, spelling and writing
- introduces words which include more advanced sounds such as chair, cloud and foil.

Written by Lucy Lyes

Encourage your child to ask for help whenever it is needed.

Say the six sounds

Say what each pair of pictures shows. Listen to the end sound that the two words share.

car   star   boy   toy

cow   bow   stir   spur

straw   saw   hair   chair

Can you think of other words that end with these sounds?

Say the words for each pair of pictures. Listen to the middle sound that the two words share.

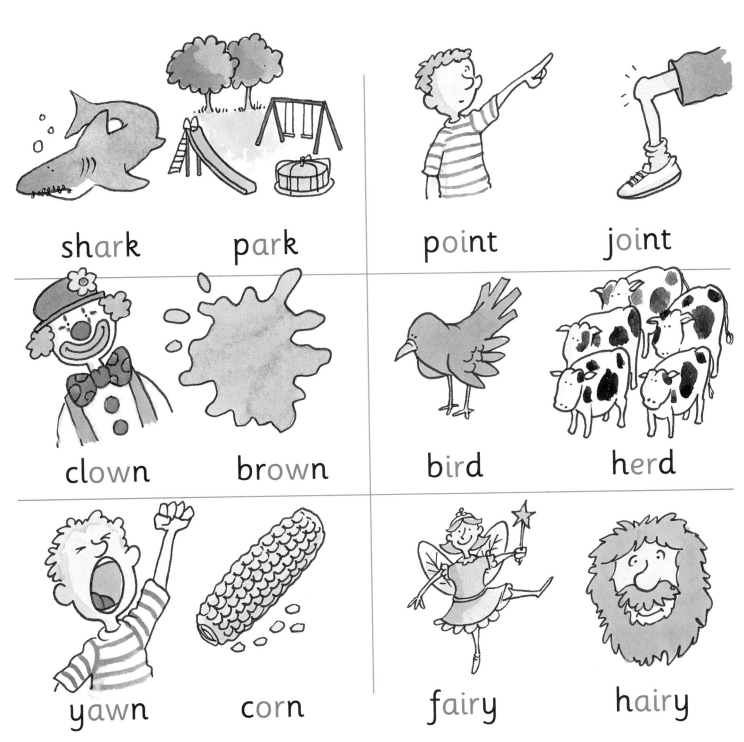

shark   park   point   joint

clown   brown   bird   herd

yawn   corn   fairy   hairy

Can you think of other words with these sounds in the middle?

Noisy Roy's page

Write the oy spelling pattern to complete each word. Say each word aloud. Can you hear the sound the oy pattern makes?

t___   b___   r___al   ___ster

The oi spelling pattern also represents this sound, but only in the middle of words. Use it to complete these words.

c___n   p___nt   t___let

j___nt   n___se   s___l

Draw a line to join the two oi words that rhyme.

Brown Mouse's page

Say the word for each picture. Listen to the sound the ow pattern makes. Choose and write the correct word under each picture.

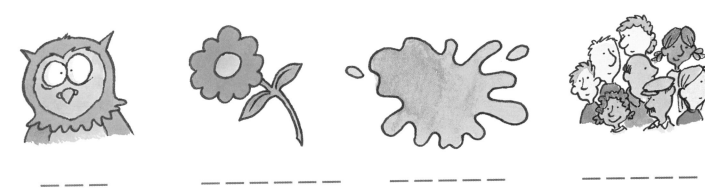

_ _ _   _ _ _ _ _ _   _ _ _ _ _   _ _ _ _ _

crowd   flower   owl   brown

The ou pattern makes the same sound. Use it to complete each of these words.

m_ _ _se   cl_ _d   h_ _se   b_ _nce

c_ _ _nt   sh_ _ _t   sp_ _t   f_ _ntain

Can you circle the two ou words that rhyme in each row?

Large Shark's page

Copy the ending of the first word in each pair to finish the second. Say the words, and listen to the sound the ar makes.

car   st___   bark   sh____

cart   d____   farm   ____

Now find the correct sticker for each of the ar words below.

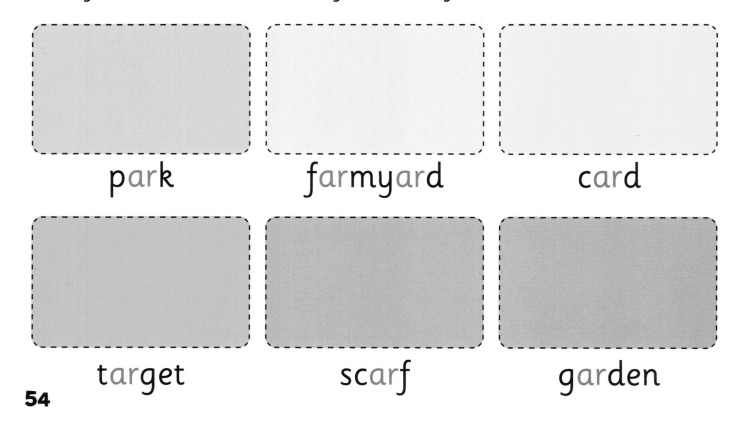

park   farmyard   card

target   scarf   garden

Curly Bird's page

Say these words and listen to the middle sound they share.
Trace over the red letters to write three patterns that can spell
this sound.

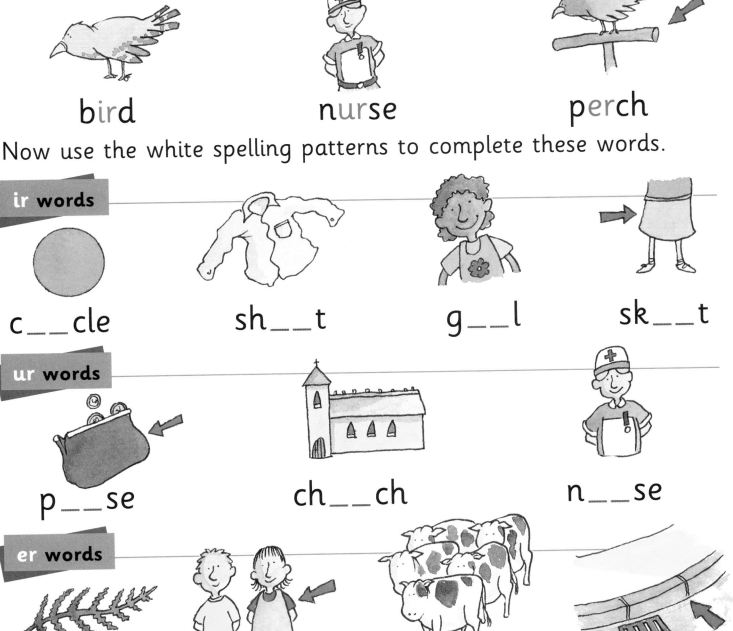

bird   nurse   perch

Now use the white spelling patterns to complete these words.

ir words

c___cle   sh___t   g___l   sk___t

ur words

p___se   ch___ch   n___se

er words

f___n   h___   h___d   k___b

Which is which?

Choose and write the correct spelling pattern to complete each of these words.

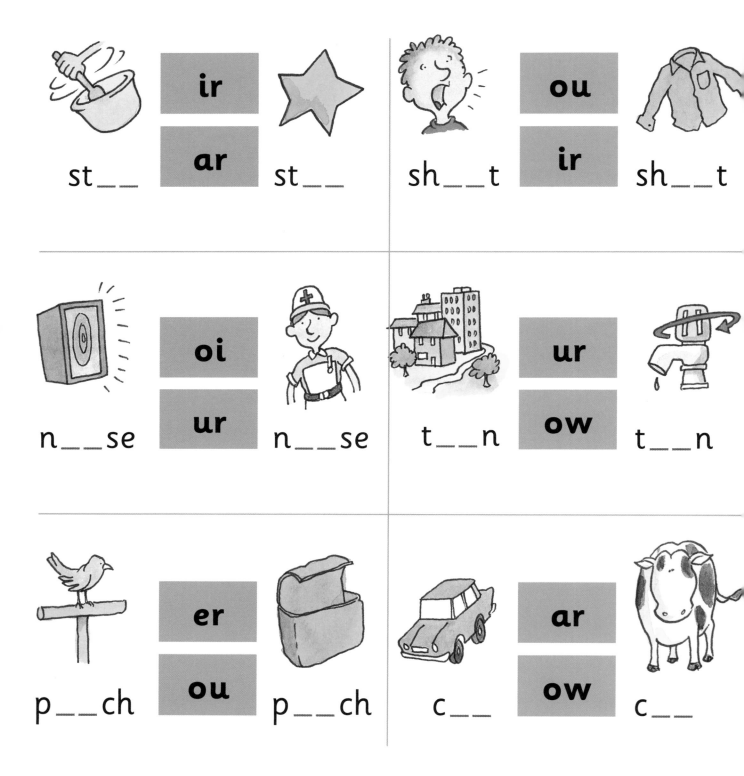

st___   **ir** / **ar**   st___

sh___t   **ou** / **ir**   sh___t

n___se   **oi** / **ur**   n___se

t___n   **ur** / **ow**   t___n

p___ch   **er** / **ou**   p___ch

c___   **ar** / **ow**   c___

Hairy Bear's page

Say these words and listen to the end sound they share. Trace over the red letters with a pencil to write three patterns that spell this sound.

b ear   ch air   squ are

Use the white spelling pattern to finish the words in each row.

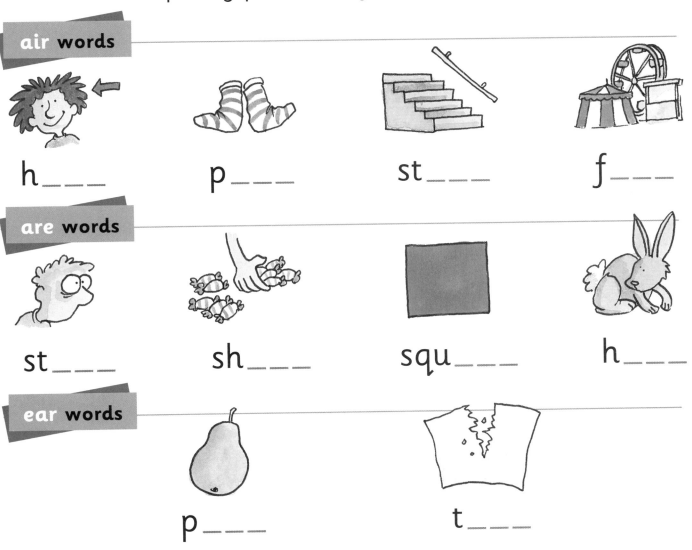

air words

h____   p____   st____   f____

are words

st____   sh____   squ____   h____

ear words

p____   t____

Short Horse's page

Look at the red spelling pattern. Read each word aloud and listen to the sound each spelling pattern makes. Find two sticker with the same spelling pattern for each row.

p**oor**

st**ore**

str**aw**

Say what you see in each picture, then use the white spelling pattern to complete each word.

or

sh__ts

st__m

ac__n

f__k

h__se

c__k

aw

h__k

l__n

cr__l

au

astron__t

s__ce

l__nch

Same spelling, different sound

The ear spelling pattern can represent another sound, too.
Say what you see below, and listen to the repeated sound.

ear   spear   beard

Write each word from the box under the correct picture to make
a rhyming list for each of the sounds the ear pattern makes.

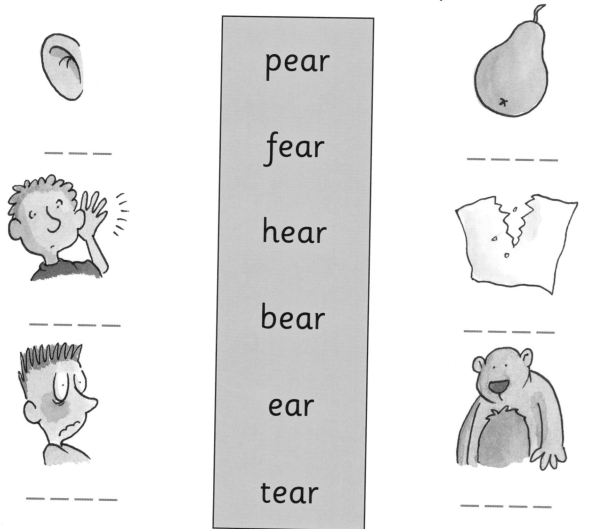

pear

fear

hear

bear

ear

tear

Pick a spelling

Choose and write the correct spelling pattern to complete each of these words.

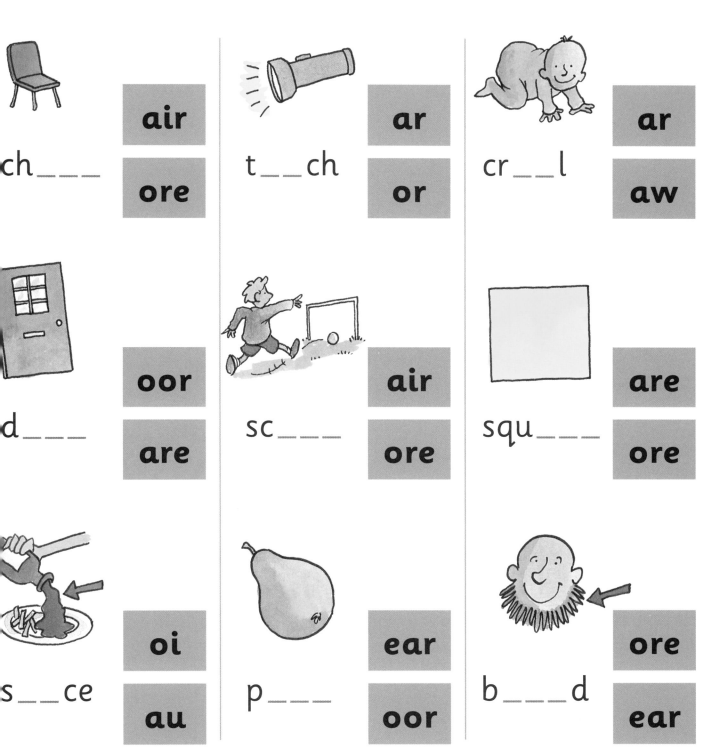

ch____   air / ore

t___ch   ar / or

cr___l   ar / aw

d____   oor / are

sc____   air / ore

squ____   are / ore

s___ce   oi / au

p____   ear / oor

b____d   ore / ear

Cow and Bear at the fair

Find the stickers to complete the story below.

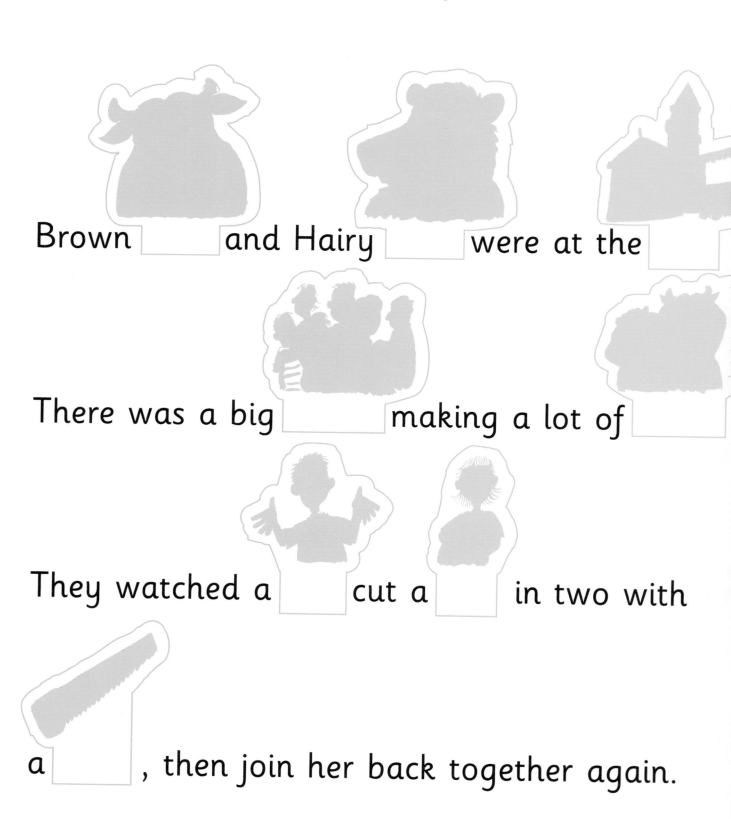

Brown [   ] and Hairy [   ] were at the [   ].

There was a big [   ] making a lot of [   ].

They watched a [   ] cut a [   ] in two with

a [   ], then join her back together again.

62

Cow threw  at a and won a .

Bear got hotdog on his fur and .

When it started to get , they went home

in Cow's sports .

Cow and Bear spelling

Can you spell the words from the story?